This Book Belongs
to
BB

GINGERBREAD BEAR

in rhyme

by Aunt Mugg

And as He passed by, He saw a man blind from birth.

And His disciples asked Him, saying, "Rabbi, who sinned, this man or His parents, that he should be born blind?"

Jesus answered, "It was neither that this man sinned, nor his parents; but it was in order that the works of God might be displayed in him."

"We must work the works of Him who sent Me, as long as it is day; night is coming, when no man can work.

"While I am in the world, I am the light of the world."

When He had said this, He spat on the ground, and made clay of the spittle, and applied the clay to his eyes,

and said to him, "Go, wash in the pool of Siloam" (which is translated, Sent). And so he went away and washed, and came back seeing.

The neighbors therefore, and those who previously saw him as a beggar, were saying, "Is not this the one who used to sit and beg?"

Others were saying, "This is he," still others were saying, "No, but he is like him." He kept saying, "I am the one."

Therefore they were saying to him, "How then were your eyes opened?"

He answered, "The man who is called Jesus made clay, and anointed my eyes, and said to me, 'Go to Siloam and wash'; so I went away and washed, and I received sight."

(John 9:1-11)

All inquiries may be directed to:
Siloam Publishing Company
P.O. Box 174
Jarrettsville, Maryland 21084

First Printing
Printed in the United States of America
ISBN 0-9668358-1-6

There's a story to tell, have you heard it before?
It's the tale of Gingerbread Bear,
Who dared to step forward
and live all her dreams
Overcoming her pain and despair?

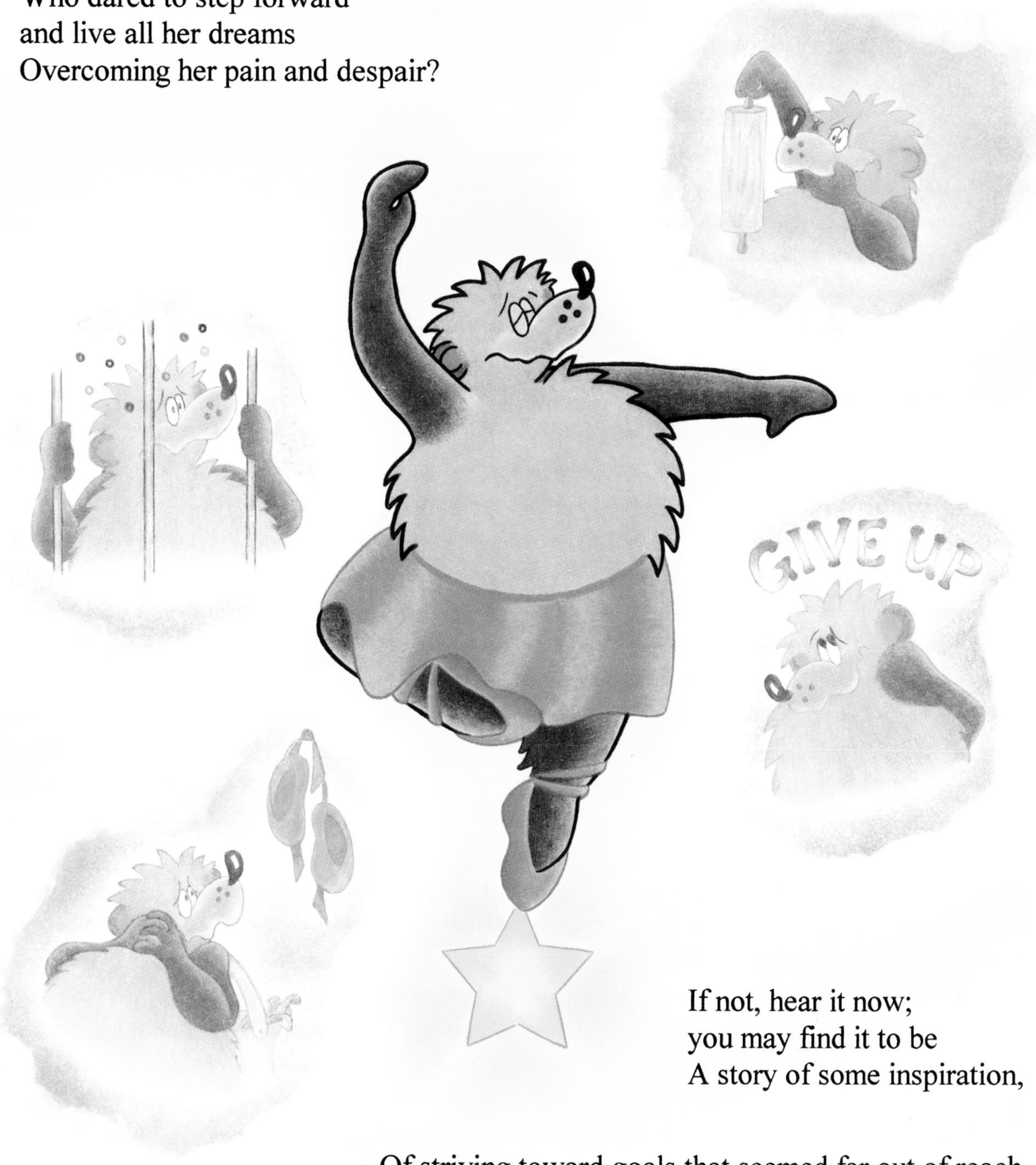

If not, hear it now;
you may find it to be
A story of some inspiration,

Of striving toward goals that seemed far out of reach
And then finally, their realization.

Madama Butterfly

Gingerbread Bear is today quite a star;
Few have a presence so grand.
With two-hundred operas, a *huge* repertoire,
Small wonder she's so in demand.
Famed opera houses all over the world
Were sold out and packed to the ceiling.
She lived and she breathed all her roles so she sang
With a fervor that left senses reeling.

starring
Gingerbread Bear
as
CIO-CIO-SAN

Lenore was courageous…
…her Carmen? Outrageous!
The bartered Marenka, indignant,

Her Martha was playful…

…Aida? So faithful,

And Ortrude? Not *quite* so malignant.

She played every role,
sometimes just filling in,
Astounding was her versatility.
Her vocal cords were, from soprano to bass,
Gymnastic in their flexibility.

But not just her 7.5 octave range…she also had mastered the dance.
Ballet performances flawlessly done were booked many years in advance.

Whatever her role,
from soprano to bass,

Whether a swan…

…or a clown,

T'was standing room only and she without fail,
Consistently brought the house down.

Yet, she once used to dance,
(but it wasn't on stage)
Just through pastures and forests
and glens.
And she once used to sing,
(but t'was not at the Met)
Just on hilltops and meadows
to friends.
And once she was famous,
but t'wasn't like now
When she blushes at whispers
and stares;
Before she had realized
her greatest of dreams
She used to bake…

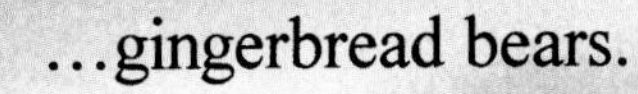

…gingerbread bears.

There once was a time
long before her acclaim,
She was only a traveling bear,
And on her back
she carried a pack
Of treats beyond compare.

Twirling about
and calling out
In a lovely, sweet voice
rich and clear,

"Come taste my delicious,
warm gingerbread bears!

They're the best you'll eat far and near!"

And running to see her from far and wide
Were forest friends loving her wares.
All of them sometime or other had tasted
Her spicy warm gingerbread bears.

Everyone spoke of her…
fast grew her fame…
And though she indeed
had no name,
Everyone knew her
because of her treats,

Thus, "Gingerbread Bear" she became.

So it happened one day that the Gingerbread Bear
Found her way into Weezy's Woods.
Her powerful voice, sweet and full, singing out,
"Gingerbread bears! Taste my goods!
Tra-la-la-la! This exquisite breeze
Chases the cobwebs away,
The birds are all singing, the sky is so blue,
What a glorious, God-given day!"
And one at a time, peeking out through the trees,
Said the Weezies, "Who *is* that? Who knows?"
Attracted to…curious…and a bit scared
Of this bear twirling 'round on her toes.

"Ho, ho!
Don't be scared!
Come on out!
Talk to me!

My name is Gingerbread Bear!"

And flipping a cookie
up out of her pack

She turned somersaults high in the air.
Catching the morsel ten feet off the ground

And never missing a beat,

She sang "Yankee Doodle" on her way down,

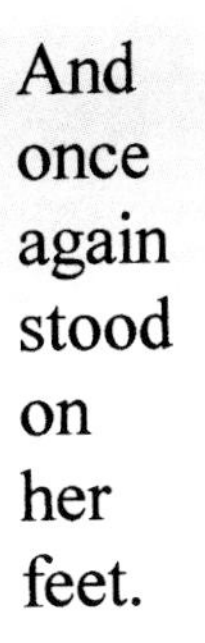

And
once
again
stood
on
her
feet.

"That was **GREAT**!"
"Can you do that again?"
"An encore!"
"You put on a magnificent show!"
"How long are you here?"
"Just where are you from?"
So much they wanted to know.

“Tut, tut!” said the bear, “Please! One at a time!
I’ll tell you my story. You’ll see!”
And proceeded to tell them her tale while she sang
And danced simultaneously.

B8

“You see,” sang the bear, “I live quite far away;
I come from a woods way out west.
I’ve always made gingerbread bears for my friends;
They’ve told me it’s what I do best.
I’d much rather do other things, like perform,
But they told me I won’t get a break.
‘So be safe,’ they all said, ‘and keep baking your bears;
This way you won’t make a mistake.’ ”

"You see, all you Weezies, I do love to sing,
I've been told I've a marvelous voice;
But my friends said my chances of singing on stage
Weren't good, so I have little choice.

'Too much competition,' they told me, they did,
And I'm *sure* that they wouldn't deceive me;
They said that it's hopeless; I'd never succeed,
Or else I would try to…believe me."

“Indeed, I believe that they’re all quite sincere
When by their advice they assert;

It’s just my welfare they’re looking out for,
They don’t want to see me get hurt.”
(Proverbs 27:6)

Before they could speak,
she sprang to her feet
And performed
a mid-air pirouette,

Then leaped toward the Weezies
and plucked up Maurice

And they pranced
through a light
minuet.

Then, light as a feather,
she floated aloft
And with hardly so much
as a glance,
She landed atop
a small cookie and did
A toe to toe
"gingerbread dance."

Her balance enthralled them,
so graceful she was;
Yes, surely from what
they could see,
Few could come close
to the things she could do
And she did them so…
…effortlessly.

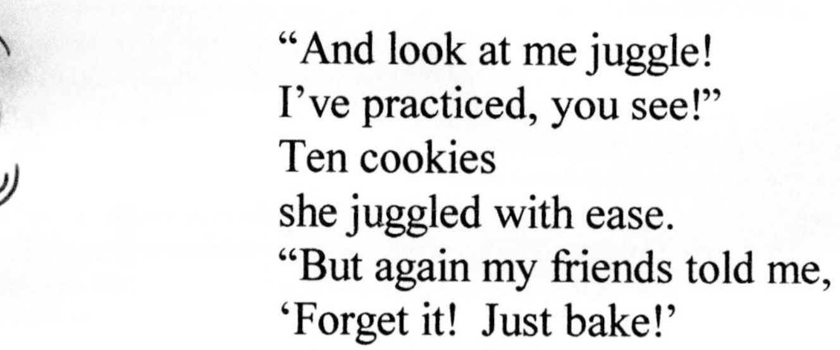

"And look at me juggle!
I've practiced, you see!"
Ten cookies
she juggled with ease.
"But again my friends told me,
'Forget it! Just bake!'
They said I can't do as I please!"

“So now here I am, baking gingerbread bears,
And I’ve come to a sort of…conclusion:
My dream does seem lofty,
perhaps they are right,
Maybe it’s all a delusion.
I do want to sing at La Scala, my friends,
But I guess that I may never do it;
That’s what my friends told me,
perhaps it *is* best,
I’ve finally resigned myself to it.”

They looked at each other,
then Willis spoke up.

"We believe that you're being deceived.
It's so very hard to break free of a lie
When once you've its poison received.
Turning your ear to a lie bears the fruit
Of a war that can never be won.
That shouldn't surprise you…
…you've lost from the start
Since you gave up before you'd begun.
Make a decision and look away now.
You might not end up on a stage…
There's no guarantee; but not trying your best
Is just locking yourself in a cage." *(Psalm 141:5a)*

"We know of a circus that's visiting here.
Audition! Sing opera and dance!
Don't let opportunity pass you by now,
This may be your very last chance!"

She sat there a moment, so perfectly still,
Uncertainty there in her eyes…
That curtain of gloom that was down for so long
Now gradually started to rise.
The truth was so powerful, piercing her heart
And exposing the lie she believed.
The scales that once covered her eyes fell away
When their love words she humbly received. *(Proverbs 15:31)*

“It’s true,” she thought pensively, “Deep down inside
My doubts and my fears are increasing.”
Now facing the truth where her focus had been
Was grievous, yet strangely…releasing.

All of those years baking gingerbread bears for which she had little affection,
But much safer then to stay right where she was, rather than facing rejection.

She knew this was wrong,
t'was the "chicken" way out,
And yes, now she had to decide:
Would she remain in that cage all her life
Wiping tears that could never be dried?

She looked at them finally and nodded her head
With this dawning new realization.
Her choice was now clear as she got to her feet
And it filled her with sweet inspiration.

"I'll do it! I'll try!

Now…what shall I sing?"

And laughing and leading the way
To the Big Top they took her, where out on the tent

Was a sign that read
"Amateur Day."

The Weezies all hugged her, then stood by her side *(Romans 12:15)*
As she sang "Un Bel Dí," and she twirled
With a heart that was bursting with freedom and joy
As she back-flipped and juggled and whirled.

Everyone loved her,
the crowd cheered and screamed;
They whistled and stomped on the floor.
And after the show
her contract was signed,
Complete with a star on her door.

"Thank-you, my friends, and you *are* my friends!"
And brushing a tear from her eye,

She hugged all the Weezies
then leaped on the train
Blowing kisses and waving goodbye.

And that was the last that they'd see her for years,
But they never forgot this dear friend
Who lived in a prison of doubt for so long,
Then broke away free in the end.

And needless to say, all the Weezies to her
Who encouraged her
right from the start,
With love and desire
to see her set free,

Would
always
be
dear
to
her
heart.
(Galatians 5:1)

There *are* times we'd all like to throw in the towel
Because of those verbal abuses;
They somehow lend credence to why we fail…so
We tend to embrace those excuses.
Things start to get fuzzy when we entertain
This "swirly," destructive intrusion;
And in no time we'll find ourselves hopelessly caught
In a cyclone of crippling confusion.

We all should be thankful for those who expose
Those dark places we would defend.
So few will risk telling us truth but indeed,
This is the mark of a friend.

And yet in this story there's one lesson more…
And that is escaping the snare
That others will set to discourage our dreams,
For in them our joy they can't share.
It's grievous that often discouragement comes
From some who resent our desire;
The flame of our dreams they would dampen with words
That sometimes extinguish our fire.

But then we all need
to be thankful for gifts,
Those God-given gifts we enjoy…
(James 1:17)

And scatter away
all those dark seeds of doubt
That once taken root
will destroy.
(1John 1:5)

Be thankful for gifts, and if chances arise
To develop them further,
explore them.

And if
peoples' comments
bear truth,
then receive…

And if otherwise, simply ignore them. *(Job 34:3)*

ITEMS OF INTEREST

Opera Roles

Cio-Cio San from Madama Butterfly
By Italian composer Giacomo Puccini (1858-1924)

Lenore from Fidelio
By German composer Ludwig van Beethoven (1770-1827)

Carmen from Carmen
By French composer Georges Bizet (1838-1875)

Marenka from The Bartered Bride
By Czech composer Bedřich Smetana (1824-1884)

Martha from Martha
By German composer Friedrich von Flotow (1812-1883)

Aïda from Aïda
By Italian composer Giuseppe Verdi (1813-1901)

Ortrude from Lohengrin
By German composer Richard Wagner (1813-1883)

Canio from Pagliacci
By Italian composer Ruggiero Leoncavallo (1858-1919)

Ballets

Sleeping Beauty
Music by Russian composer Peter Ilyitch Tschaikowsky (1840-1893)

Le Corsaire
Music by French composer Adolphe Charles Adam (1803-1856)

Cinderella
Music by Russian composer Sergei Prokofiev (1891-1953)

The Dying Swan
Music by French composer Camille Saint-Saëns (1834-1921)

(The Dying Swan by Camille Saint-Saëns is not to be confused with Swan Lake by Russian composer Peter Ilyitch Tschaikowsky)

Did you know…?

The Metropolitan Opera House (the Met) is located at Lincoln Center in New York City, New York
Fidelio was the only opera Ludwig van Beethoven composed
La Scala is a very famous opera house in Milan, Italy
"Un Bel Dí" is a famous soprano aria from the opera Madama Butterfly
SRO means Standing Room Only
The word pagliacci is Italian meaning "clowns"
The words le corsaire are French meaning "the pirate"

REFERENCED SCRIPTURES

Faithful are the wounds of a friend, but deceitful are the kisses of an enemy.
(Proverbs 27:6)

Let the righteous smite me in kindness and reprove me; It is oil upon the head; do not let my head refuse it.
(Psalm 141:5a)

He whose ear listens to the life-giving reproof will dwell among the wise.
(Proverbs 15:31)

Rejoice with those who rejoice, and weep with those who weep.
(Romans 12:15)

It was for freedom that Christ set us free; therefore keep standing firm and do not be subject again to a yoke of slavery. (Galatians 5:1)

Every good thing bestowed and every perfect gift is from above, coming down from the Father of lights, with whom there is no variation, or shifting shadow. (James 1:17)

And this is the message we have heard from Him and announce to you, that God is light, and in Him there is no darkness at all. (1John 1:5)

"For the ear tests words as the palate tastes food." (Job 34:3)